GONZO..SNARF.. HIP...YOWZA..AH WANT ME WOODY BACK YEAH..

I WOULD JUST LIKE TO DISPEL THESE MALICIOUS RUMOURS THAT I MISTREAT MY STAFF.. I HAVE NEVER, BEATEN, WHIPPED.. OR PHYSICALLY ABUSED MY STAFF.. EVER!

THAT'S HIS JOB!

TIMESLIP. 17. PRUDHOE PLACE. N'CASTLE PHONE 2 61 91 73

HOLIDAY SPECIAL

Written and drawn by
Chris Donald (Editor)
Simon Donald (Assistant Editor)
Graham Dury (Deputy Editor)
Simon Thorp (Co-Assistant Sub Deputy Editor)
and David Jones
Photography by Colin Davison

Published in Great Britain by John Brown Publishing Limited, Suite 216, Canalot Studios, 222 Kensal Road, London W10 5BN.

ISBN 1 870 870 01 8

You can write to Viz Comic at P.O. Box 1PT, Newcastle upon Tyne. NE99 1PT providing you've got nothing better to do.

'Having a Lovely Time'
PRESENTED BY
ROGER MELLIE
THE MAN ON THE TELLY

6

Jack Black AND HIS DOG SILVER IN THE CASE OF THE BOOK SMUGGLER

The summer holidays were here at last and young Jack Black and his dog, Silver were staying at Aunt Meg's clifftop cottage in Cornwall.

One afternoon, Jack Black and his dog, Silver were enthralled in an exciting jungle adventure film on the television.

GOSH! WHAT AN EXCITING FILM, SILVER.

TARZAN OF THE APES

THAT WAS A GOOD FILM, AUNT MEG. HOW CAN I FIND OUT MORE ABOUT JUNGLE ANIMALS?

WHY DON'T YOU POP DOWN TO THE VILLAGE LIBRARY, JACK?

HMM! I'M SURE THAT THE BISCUIT TIN WAS FULL THIS MORNING!

Young Jack Black and his dog, Silver set off towards the village library as fast as their legs could carry them.

COME ON, SILVER! LETS FIND OUT MORE ABOUT JUNGLE ANIMALS.

In the library...

HELLO, MR BROWN. WE'D LIKE A BIG PICTURE BOOK ABOUT JUNGLE ANIMALS, PLEASE.

GOSH!

I'M SORRY, YOUNG JACK, BUT AS YOU CAN SEE, WE HAVE NO BOOKS LEFT WHATSOEVER! THE VILLAGERS MUST BE DOING AN AWFUL LOT OF READING!

Later on, Jack returned home for tea.

...AND WHEN WE GOT TO THE LIBRARY, ALL THE BOOKS HAD DISAPPEARED!

TALKING OF THINGS DISAPPEARING, HAS ANYONE SEEN THE CHELSEA BUNS I BAKED THIS MORNING.

The next day...

COME ON, SILVER, LET'S GO TO THE BEACH AND COLLECT INTERESTING SHELLS!

BEACH BOOKS

CRIKEY, SILVER! A BOOKSHOP ON THE BEACH! HOW PECULIAR!

9

Jack asked the ice cream seller about the mysterious bookshop.

THAT BOOKSHOP IS PUTTING ME OUT OF BUSINESS, JACK! NO ONE BUYS MY ICE CREAMS ANY LONGER!

COME ON, SILVER! I'LL RACE YOU TO THE CLIFFS! LAST ONE THERE IS A BAD EGG!

HEY, SILVER! WHAT HAVE YOU FOUND?

GOSH, LOOK! A SECRET CAVE WITH A STAIRWAY! LET'S SEE WHERE IT GOES!

Halfway up the stairway...

CRUMBS! WHAT'S THIS, SILVER? IT LOOKS LIKE SOME SORT OF BOOK!

At the top of the dark stairway, Jack and Silver came across a mysterious door.

I WONDER WHERE THAT LEADS TO!

GOSH! THE LIBRARY!

On his way home, Jack wondered what the library would want with a secret tunnel leading to the beach.

HMM! I WONDER!

Jack's Uncle Dick was a brilliant scientist and that evening, Jack showed him the mysterious object he had found in the cave.

NOW, LET ME SEE!

THIS APPEARS TO BE SOME SORT OF BOOK...

...AND JUDGING BY THE STAMP HERE, I'D SAY IT WAS A LIBRARY BOOK!

GOSH, UNCLE DICK! YOU'RE BRILLIANT!

Later, at tea time...

I'M AFRAID THERE'S NOTHING FOR TEA TONIGHT, JACK! THE FRENCH FANCIES I BAKED THIS MORNING HAVE ALL DISAPPEARED!

NOT TO WORRY, AUNT MEG! SILVER AND I HAVE DETECTIVE WORK TO DO!

Once again, Jack and Silver made their way towards the beach.

Jack and Silver hid themselves behind a large rock overlooking the entrance to the secret cave.

Presently, a shadowy figure emerged.

GOSH, SILVER! IT'S MR BROWN, THE LIBRARIAN.

Suddenly...

WOOF!!

CRIKEY, SILVER! A CRAB HAS BITTEN YOU, CAUSING YOU TO BARK AND WE HAVE BEEN SPOTTED BY MR BROWN, THE LIBRARIAN!!

SO, YOU AND YOUR MEDDLING DOG HAVE UNCOVERED MY LITTLE PLAN!*

*The Plan: Mr. Brown the librarian had been abusing his position at the library by smuggling books to his beach bookshop. Because his was the only bookshop on the beach, people had no choice but to pay the outrageous prices he charged, thus putting the ice cream seller out of business.

Mr Brown wasted no time in bundling the detective duo into the back of his waiting lorry.

TONIGHT I'M LEAVING FOR A BOOK FAIR IN EASTERN EUROPE AND YOU'RE COMING WITH ME! YOU AND YOUR MEDDLING DOG WILL NEVER BE SEEN AGAIN!!

After loading up his books, Mr Brown set off for the local abandoned airfield...

...but Jack had a plan.

Shortly...

HELLO, WHAT'S ALL THIS THEN?

BOOKS! THAT'S FUNNY! 'JACK AND THE BEANSTALK' AND 'KIDNAPPED'!

11

Minutes later, the police were heading for the airfield in a fast car.

But as they approched the airfield, Mr Brown, an accomplished pilot, had already got his plane airborne.

P.C. Barnett was a fine marksman and one shot was all it took to put a stop to Mr Brown's evil plan.

Its evil pilot dead, the plane spun hopelessly out of control.

Meanwhile, in the plane...

Carefully following the instructions in the book, Jack was able to bring the aircraft under control...

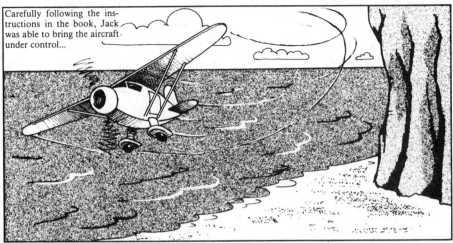

...and make a spectacular landing perilously close to the cliff edge.

Later, Jack was back safe and sound in Aunt Meg's cottage.

Suddenly...

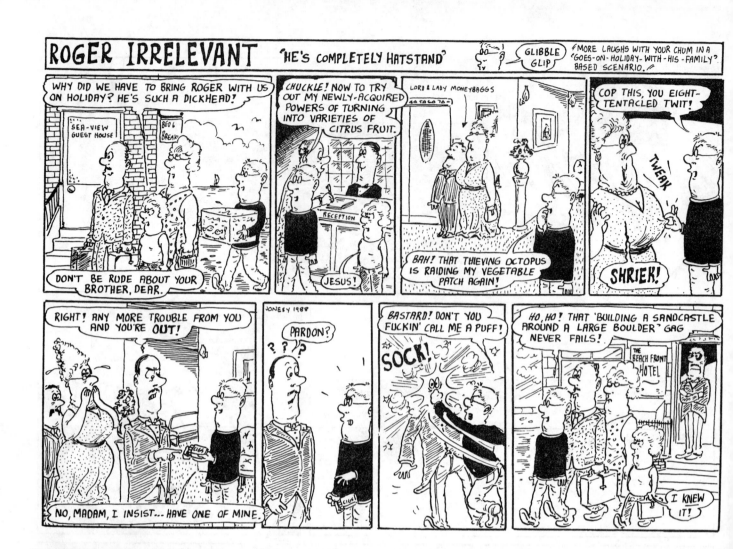

ON THE BEACH PERSON SPOTTING GAME

It's a lovely hot summers day and lots of Viz characters have gone to the beach. Some are well known, others not so familiar. Can you name them all? If you can, big deal. If you can't, the answers are on page 54.

There was no room for love at the...

HEARTBREAK HOTEL

But Sandra had no luck ...

Eventually she made her way back to Ray's hotel

16

Still unable to find a room, Sarah settled down for the night on a park bench not far from the seafront

I JUST HOPE RAY'S ALRIGHT ON HIS OWN. GOODNIGHT RAY ... I'LL SEE YOU TOMORROW MY LOVE.

And as she drifted off to sleep, the sound of distant waves echoing in her ears, she dreamt of dancing arm in arm with Ray on the warm, sunny sands ...

The next morning she was up early for her rendezvous with Ray

WHAT A LOVELY DAY FOR A ROMANTIC STROLL ALONG THE BEACH!

Six hours later

THAT'S ODD. RAY'S NOT USUALLY LATE. I HOPE NOTHING'S HAPPENED TO HIM.

Eventually ...

RAY! THANK HEAVENS, I WAS SO WORRIED ABOUT YOU!

SORRY LOVE, I'VE ONLY JUST GOT UP. I WAS UP DRINKING TILL FOUR THIS MORNING!

IT'S TOO LATE TO GO TO THE BEACH, SO WHY DON'T WE GO TO THE PICTURES INSTEAD. APPARENTLY THERE'S A REALLY ROMANTIC FILM ON ...

OH, SORRY LOVE. I CAN'T. I MET THIS GIRL IN THE HOTEL LAST NIGHT AND I PROMISED I'D TAKE HER OUT FOR A MEAL.

OH ... WELL ... IN THAT CASE, I'LL JUST GO FOR A STROLL ON MY OWN OR SOMETHING THEN.

DON'T BE SILLY LOVE! LOOK, HERE'S A POUND. GO AND GET YOURSELF SOME CHIPS, AND I'LL SEE YOU TOMORROW.

Later ...

THANKS FOR THE CHIPS RAY. THEY'RE LOVELY. IF ONLY YOU WERE HERE TO SHARE THEM WITH ME.

BUT I CAN'T EXPECT TO OWN YOU, CAN I? BEING ABLE TO TRUST EACH OTHER CAN ONLY STRENGTHEN OUR LOVE

The next day Sarah went straight to Ray's hotel

IT'S ANOTHER PERFECT DAY — JUST RIGHT FOR A STROLL ALONG THE BEACH! I HOPE RAY IS OUT OF BED.

HE MUST STILL BE IN HIS ROOM. I THINK I'LL SURPRISE HIM!

But she was in for a big surprise

17

But when Ray arrived he was not alone

Soon ...

In a cosy romantic restaurant ...

18

CD 5.88 Photography by C.W. Davison. Thanks to the Aabba Guest House, Whitley Bay and the Whitley Bay Tourist Board.

FINBARR HOLDS HIS OWN

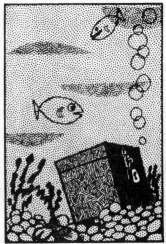

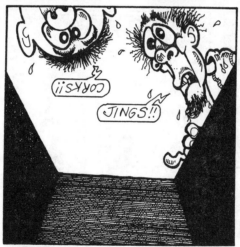

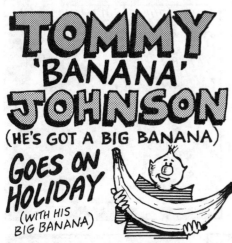

TERRY FUCKWITT'S HOLIDAY CLOTHING TEASER

Terry has just been swimming in the sea and, oh dear, he's put the wrong clothes on. You can guess who's clothes Terry is wearing (if you've got nothing better to do.) The answers are on page 54.

You have drunk 25 pints of fizzy Spanish lager and you are going to be horrendously sick any minute. Can you negotiate the maze, avoiding the Spanish riot policeman and the toy donkey seller and reach the toilet before you make a pavement pizza? To add realism to this game you may wish to drink 25 pints of lager before beginning the puzzle.

Who's behind Shakey's green doors?

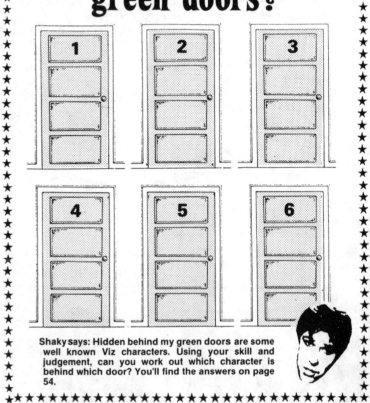

Shaky says: Hidden behind my green doors are some well known Viz characters. Using your skill and judgement, can you work out which character is behind which door? You'll find the answers on page 54.

Tommy 'Banana' Johnson's Holiday Insults Game

Can you think of six different insulting names which we often use when refering to the inhabitants of the following six countries? The insulting name for each will fit into the corresponding line in the grid below, and when you've got them all the letters in the shaded boxes will reveal an item that Tommy 'Banana' Johnson would probably take with him on holiday.

The answers are on page 54.

1. FRANCE   2. SWITZERLAND   3. ITALY
4. AUSTRALIA   5. GERMANY   6. BELGUIM

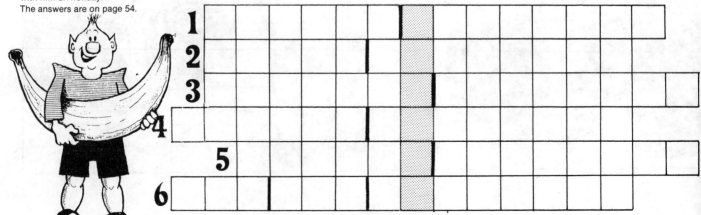

BUSTER GONAD
& his unfeasibly large TESTICLES
and
FELIX
& his amazing UNDERPANTS
in
BUSTER & FELIX GO TO THE SEASIDE

SO...

HEY, BUSTER, THAT LOOKS LIKE FUN! LET'S HAVE A GO!

I'D LIKE TO HIRE A WIND-SURFBOARD, PLEASE!

HIRE SHOP

NOT FROM MY SHOP YOU WONT. THOSE TESTICLES OF YOURS ARE TOTALLY UNSEA-WORTHY! YOU'D BE A DANGER TO SHIPPING, YOU BIG BOLLOCKED BUFFOON!!

HA! THIS TESTICLE/UNDERPANT COMBINATION IS JUST THE TICKET

HA!!

IF ONLY IT WAS MORE WINDY!!

BR-R-R-R-RAP!

PHUT!

EH!! WASSAT NOISE!?!

NO, IT'S...

IT SOUNDS LIKE A MOTORBIKE WITHOUT A SILENCER...

...JOHNNY FARTPANTS!!!

HEY, JOHNNY! WE NEED YOUR HELP! ANY CHANCE OF A GENTLE SEA BREEZE!?!

SO...

POP!

CHUFF!

45

JOHNNY FARTPANTS' EUR

Hi folks! Johnny Fartpants here, your rumbling bottomed chum. Whenever you go on holiday it always pays to know which foreign foods to eat in order to get that all important holiday pumping power! All too often holidaymakers go abroad without having done their homework, and they often end up having a trumpless trip to Tripoli or a fart-free fortnight in France. What could be worse? So here's a guide to continental cuisine that will help YOU to get more farts for your franc or more guffs per guilda next time you go abroad.

Have a nice holiday, and remember — keep pumping!

Johnny Fartpants

FRANCE

Despite not being the most prolific pumpsters in Europe, the French make up for lack of gusto with rich and aromatic botty-burps, or "les petit vents" as they might say themselves. Their constant diet of strong coffee, frog's legs, onions, garlic and peculiarly shaped loafs of bread leave the French with weak but wonderfully flavoured farts. Take an early evening stroll along the Champs Elyseé, past a myriad of romantic restaurants, and smell for yourself what the French do best.

PUMP POINTS: 🌬️🌬️🌬️

ITALY

Rome truely is the 'City of Farts', and is the old saying goes, when in Rome do as the Romans. Drop into any Italian restaurant and the pump potential is enormous. Their weighty pasta dishes will line your stomach like lead, and you'll be farting like a Ferrari before the ice cream trolley has arrived.

PUMP POINTS: 🌬️🌬️🌬️🌬️🌬️

GERMANY

Despite losing two consecutive world wars and the 1966 World Cup final, the Germans still haven't forgotten how to fart. The boffing bosh owe all of their success to the lethal combination of BANGERS and BEER! Yes, the sour faced krauts stuff themselves with sausages, guzzle gallons of fizzy lager, and let-off in their lehderhosen until the early hours of the morning.

When in Germany, try eating a selection of sausages, the bigger the better, and wash them down with a few pints of pils. Then make your way to the hotel swimming pool, and you'll soon see why the Germans always get the pool to themselves.

PUMP POINTS: 🌬️🌬️🌬️

HOLLAND

It is often said that if everyone in Holland farted at once, sufficient electricity would be generated through their vast network of windmills to make enough cheese to last the entire population a year! But cheese is by no means the most fart-productive of food stuffs. When you're in Amsterdam, choose your cheese with care. Gouda won't give you many guffs per gram. Try Wensleydale, and you'll soon be delivering dykebusters that will have the Dutchmen clattering in their clogs!

PUMP POINTS: 🌬️🌬️🌬️

SWEDEN

Farting has been illegal in Sweden since 1975.

PUMP POINTS: NIL

NORWAY

As you probably know, Norweigians spend most of their time eating fish in their long, thin country. As a result, farts are few and far between in the fjords. But if you've already booked a holiday in Norway, don't despair. The geography of the country could come to your rescue! Indeed, the steep, stoney walls of the deep and desolate fjords can channel a good chuff for many a mile. For example, if your backside barked in Bergen, the echo would travel to Trondhiem and back before you'd had a chance to pull up your trousers.

A useful trick in most Scandinavian countries is to eat raw fish and seaweed then jump up and down a bit until you feel one coming on.

PUMP POINTS: 🌬️

SWITZERLAND

The Swiss are probably better known for their confectionery, watch making and banking industries than they are for their botty burping, possibly due to their unimaginative diet of white chocolate and muesli. But if you look carefully, there are more inspiring dishes available in the Alps. Try goat curry with turnips, served with garlic and peppers. Or pickled eggs. But be warned — there is strictly no pumping on the piste.

BARK!

The danger of causing an avalanche is simply too great, and in many ski resorts police will insist you take 'Windcheaters' or a similar pump preventative before taking to the slopes.

PUMP POINTS: 🌬️🌬️

DENMARK

Denmark is a country steeped in trumping tradition going back to Viking days. Up until around 300AD they performed religious rasping rituals in order to please their Gods, among them 'Thor' who was originally the God of Farting. Modern day historians have since adapted this to 'God of Thunder'. Even today these ceremonies still take place in some of Denmarks remote coastal communities. One theory recently put forward to explain how the Vikings succeeded in making their

FARTING GUIDE

EUROPE AT A GLANCE

PUMPS PER PLATEFUL

☐	0
▨	1 - 25
▦	26 - 50
▨	51 - 75
▩	76 - 100

epic journey from the Norse lands to the Americas is that they used pump power to propel their Long Boats across the Atlantic. Among the foods that they would no doubt have eaten to achieve this effect was Skoghiem — a traditional Danish delicacy of bacon and raisins rolled in pastry. Skoghiem, loosely translated means 'bringer of wind', and is still available in most of Denmarks restaurants and supermarkets.

PUMP POINTS:

SPAIN

The traditional Spanish diet of healthy food once made them the farting laughing stock of Europe. Indeed, farting wasn't introduced into the country until the late 18th century when the Spanish armada brought beans and cabbage water back from Latin America.

Even today, the traditional fare of paella and seafood can leave the pump-hungry holidaymaker high and dry. But the millions of British tourists who flock to Spain each year need not worry — pump prospects are improving! Good old British beans are now widely available in all of the countries major tourist centres!

PUMP POINTS: ✿ ✿

BELGIUM

There's very little jiggery pumpery goes on in Belgium due to the blandness of their diet. Fill up with Belgian buns and biscuits. Plenty of these can induce a moderate wind flow in some people, but don't expect anything spectacular. The results won't be anything to write home about.

PUMP POINTS: ✿

ROGER IRRELEVANT

AFTER BEING ATTACKED BY A RADIOACTIVE LEOPARD, 19-YEAR-OLD **LUCY WATKINS** DIES INSTANTLY... WITH THE RESULT THAT YOUNG **ROGER IRRELEVANT**, WHOM SHE NEVER MET, DEVELOPS STRANGE TROMBONE-LIKE POWERS....

ANSWERS
from pages 14 and 34

FUCKWITT'S CLOTHING COCK-UP

Terry was wearing (left to right) Roger Mellie, Biffa Bacon, the Doctor, Felix and the Pathetic Shark's clothing.

SHAKEY'S GREEN DOOR MYSTERY

The following characters were hidden behind Shaky's green doors: 1. Buster Gonad, 2. Johnny Fartpants, 3. Nobody, 4. The Parkie, 5. Johnny Fartpants again, 6. Johnny Fartpants AND Sid the Sexist. Did you get them all right?

INSULT GRID

1	F	R	E	N	C	H	B	A	S	T	A	R	D	S
2	S	W	I	S	S	B	A	S	T	A	R	D	S	
3	I	T	A	L	I	A	N	B	A	S	T	A	R	D	S
4	A	U	S	S	I	E	B	A	S	T	A	R	D	S
5	G	E	R	M	A	N	B	A	S	T	A	R	D	S
6	B	I	G	F	A	T	B	A	S	T	A	R	D	S

ON THE BEACH

Foreground (left to right): Big Vern, Ted Dempster, Frankie Feel, Tina's Tits, Lonely Sidney Sidebottom, Hugh Phamism, Careless McKenzie, Colin the amiable Crocodile, Billy Bound, Timothy Potter, Captain Magnetic, Mr Gimlet. Middle ground: Willy Banks, Mike Smitt, Brown Bottle, Hamilton Winterbottom, Billy's Bollocks, Helpful Herbert, Odd Job Bob (in high chair), Mr Logic, Albert O'Balsam. At ice cream stall: Billy Bananahead and Tommy 'Banana' Johnson (hiding behind), Bert the Burglar (on roof), Roger Mellie (serving) and in queue Sid the Sexist, Mrs Brady the old lady, Lucky Frank, Paul Whicker, Mr Crazy Face, Peter Pretend, Tommy Brown, Billy Bloater, Buster Gonad. In the distance: Tex Wade (on horse) and Hector the collector (with his metal detector), Johnny X (Fulchester United's invisable striker). In the sea: Flash Harry, Dr Sex, Mickey the Martian, Finbarr Saunders, Felix and the Pathetic Sharks. Total 42.

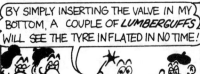

58

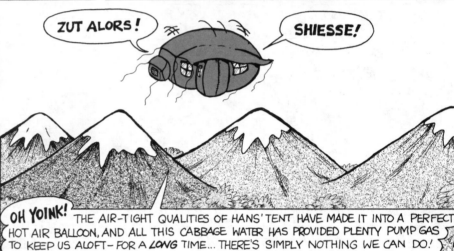

64

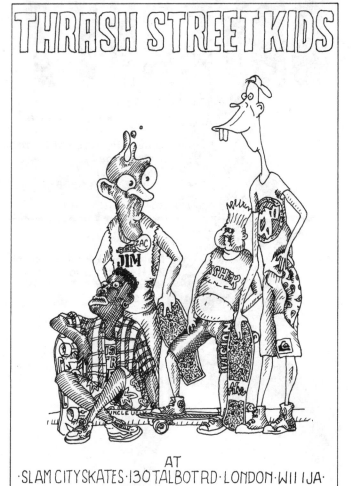